Roger
Lancelyn Green

Four Great Greek Myths

D1136846

PENGUIN BOOKS

PENGUIN BOOKS

Published by the Penguin Group
Penguin Books Ltd, 27 Wrights Lane, London w8 5tz, England
Penguin Books USA Inc., 375 Hudson Street, New York, New York 10014, USA
Penguin Books Australia Ltd, Ringwood, Victoria, Australia
Penguin Books Canada Ltd, 10 Alcorn Avenue, Toronto, Ontario, Canada m4v 3b2
Penguin Books (NZ) Ltd, 182–190 Wairau Road, Auckland 10, New Zealand

Penguin Books Ltd, Registered Offices: Harmondsworth, Middlesex, England

First published in *Tales of the Greek Heroes* in Puffin Books 1958

This collection published in Penguin Books 1996
1 3 5 7 9 10 8 6 4 2

Copyright © Roger Lancelyn Green, 1958
All rights reserved

Set in 12.5/13.5pt Bembo Monotype
Typeset by Datix International Limited, Bungay, Suffolk
Printed in England by Clays Ltd, St Ives plc

Contents

The Coming of the Immortals

IF ever you are lucky enough to visit the beautiful land of Greece you will find a country haunted by more than three thousand years of history and legend.

The towering mountains slope steeply into the bluest of blue seas, and between the mountains lie valleys green and silver with the leaves of a million olive trees; golden with corn in the early summer, and then brown and white as the hot sun dries all up until the wide rivers become tinkling streams wandering in great courses of grey and yellow stones.

In winter and early spring the mountains are clothed with snow; mist hides the higher lands, and the rivers are roaring torrents racing down into the great gulfs and bays which break up Greece into little divisions as surely as the mighty mountains do.

As you wander through Greece in the late spring you are back in those ancient days the moment you leave the towns behind. Up on the green slopes below the towering heights of the great mountains, of Parnassus or Taygetus or Cithaeron, you can sit and dream yourself back into the time when you might expect to meet an Immortal on the mountain, in the olive-groves, or in the lonely valleys.

Far away a shepherd pipes to his flock, magic notes stealing up through the warm silence: surely that is Pan, half-goat, half-human, who guarded the shepherds of old?

Among the olive leaves stand the broken columns of temples, grey, or white, or golden-yellow: everyone has a tale to tell – a legend, a story, or an actual history.

Over the blue sea, with its streaks like purple wine, lie islands dotted away into the distance: and they too have each a tale to tell. It may be Delos, perhaps: no one lives on it now, but the ruins of cities and temples, harbours and theatres, cluster from the shore to the hill top on which Apollo the Shining One and his sister Artemis the Maiden Huntress were born. Or it may be rocky, rugged Ithaca, from which Odysseus sailed to the siege of Troy, and found again after ten years' wandering over strange and dragon-haunted seas.

With all the breath-taking beauty of Greece round about them, it is hardly wonderful that the ancient Greeks felt that the mountains and the valleys, the woods and streams, the very sea itself, were peopled with Immortals. There were wood-nymphs among the trees and water-nymphs in the rivers – fairies of human size who did not die and had powers which mortals do not possess. There were sea-nymphs too – mermaids, though not all of them had tails – and strange sea-beings, who might be cruel and fierce even as the sea was fierce and cruel when the storms arose. And the sea must have a King, more powerful even than the nymphs, the Immortal called Poseidon who might come up through the waters in his chariot drawn by white horses, waving his trident – the three-pronged spear which was his sceptre, or sign of power.

On land also there were Immortal powers. Apollo, shining like the sun, who was also the lord of music and poetry; Artemis the Huntress 3 who guarded all wild things; fierce Ares the war-lord, whose terrible shout might ring across the field of battle when the spears were flying and the swords of bronze or iron clanged on the shields and helmets; Athena, Immortal Lady of wisdom; the kind Mother Goddess, Demeter, who caused the corn to grow and the young lambs to be born, with her lovely daughter Persephone who had to spend half the year in the kingdom of the dead when dark winter was spread over the earth.

Then there was Aphrodite, Immortal Lady of Beauty and Love, with Eros her son who shot the invisible arrows that made a young man or girl fall in love; there was Hephaestus, more skilled than any mortal man in working with bronze and gold and iron, whose forge was beneath the island of Lemnos, with a volcano as his furnace-chimney; there was Hermes of the winged-heels, swift messenger, more cunning than any human; there was Dionysus who gave such power to the grapes that they could be brewed into wine to be a joy and a comfort to mankind; and there was the quiet Hestia, Lady of the home and guardian of the hearth – for the hearth was the heart of the home in the days when fire was difficult to make.

All these, and more, were the Immortals, and their powers were great. But they too must surely obey laws and have a ruler set over them – and this was Zeus, the King of Heaven and of Earth, who wielded the thunderbolt, and was father of Mortals and of Immortals; and his Queen was Hera, Lady of Marriage and guardian of children. Zeus had power over all Immortals, though he seldom exercised it over his brothers, Poseidon, Lord of the Sea, and Hades, Lord of the Dead, whose kingdom of shadows was thought to be beneath the earth.

The Greeks called these Immortals the 'Gods', and worshipped them, making sacrifices to them at their particular shrines: Zeus at Olympia, Apollo at Delphi, Athena at Athens, and so on. When they began to tell the stories about them they had very little idea of what gods should be, and quite naturally pictured them as very like themselves, but much more powerful, more beautiful, and more free. Nor did it seem wrong to them to imagine that gods and goddesses could be cruel, or mean, deceitful, selfish, jealous, or even wicked, according to our ideas, and as they themselves would have thought if ordinary men and women had done as the gods did.

Another trouble was that the Greeks in each of the little kingdoms and cities, and in the islands, made up different stories more or less without knowing what was being told over the sea, or beyond the mountains. Then, later, when minstrels travelled from place to place, and writing became more common, and people began to meet those from other parts of the Greek world, they found that many of the stories did not agree.

'Hera is the wife of Zeus,' the people of Argolis would say. 'Nonsense!' the Arcadians would answer. 'He married Maia, and they had a son called Hermes!' 'What are you talking about?' the people of Delphi or Delos would protest: 'The wife of Zeus is called Leto, and they had two children called Apollo and Artemis!'

6   Well, there was only one thing for it: they had

to agree that Zeus must have had several wives! But Hera, as the most important of the Immortals, was obviously the real Queen of Heaven – and, as a woman would be, she was jealous!

In the earliest days the Greeks themselves often had several wives, as the people of Egypt did, and as the Turks and the Indians did until quite recently. In Greece, however, there was usually one real wife, and the others were captives taken in war, who were treated more and more as mere slaves; well looked after, but obliged to do just as they were told.

So it was not difficult to think of Zeus or Apollo behaving in much the same way as such a King of Athens as Theseus: and of course, over in Asia, kings always had many wives. That was where Troy was, so naturally King Priam had fifty sons, and Hecuba, the Queen of Troy, was simply his chief wife.

Each of the little Greek kingdoms, or city-states, had its own Royal Family; and each Royal Family liked to trace its descent back to one of the gods. It was much the same in England a thousand years ago: Alfred the Great was said to be descended from Odin, who held just the same place among the Saxons and the Danes as Zeus did among the Greeks. Indeed, if we believe the old writers of the Middle Ages, our own Royal Family, right down to the present Queen herself, can trace its descent from Odin on the one hand, and from Antenor who was the cousin of Priam of Troy, on the other!

Certainly Hera had some reason to be jealous – and she was very jealous indeed, or so the stories tell us – of Zeus's mortal wives: and he had one in nearly every kingdom, just as sailors were said to have a wife in every port!

When the Greeks began to tell stories of the gods and goddesses, they had not become very civilized, so the legends seemed quite normal and credible to them. But as time went on, and the Greeks thought and learned more and more, some at least of them began to wonder about many of the stories: they began to realize that there was only one real God, and that he was good – better than any man could be.

Surely, however, this God must be Zeus: therefore Zeus himself must have become better and better, and have learnt by suffering until he understood what Mercy really meant.

Then the story-tellers realized that this fitted in rather well with the oldest of the stories about the gods. For in the very early days, before Zeus came, there were other gods – terrible creatures who were hardly people at all – who were as cruel and as dreadful as a tempest or an earthquake, as a tidal wave or an erupting volcano. These, in the earliest stories of all, those made by savage ancestors ages before, were the children of the Sky and the Earth. They were Giants and Titans, terrible ogres and trolls with many hands, or snake-like tails; and the most terrible of them was called Cronos – and he was the father of the real gods, of Zeus, Poseidon, Hades, and of the goddesses Hera, Hestia, and Demeter.

We need not try to imagine what Cronos was like. The Greeks who invented the stories about him cannot have done so. His name means Time – but it was only the Romans who began to picture him as kindly old Father Time, with his scythe and his hourglass.

The original Cronos was horribly different. He had a scythe, indeed, or rather a sickle – but he used it to cut pieces off his father Uranus, or Sky!

'You may be our ruler now!' Sky told him. 'But your children will treat you just as you have treated us and worse. They will bind you in a terrible prison, and one of them will rule instead of you!' And what Sky said, Earth said also, and Cronos knew that Earth cannot tell lies.

'We'll see about that!' roared Cronos, and he began to swallow his children as soon as they were born – just as Time swallows up the years, one after another.

First he swallowed Hestia, and then Demeter and Hera, and after them Hades and Poseidon.

This was too much for his wife, Rhea, although she was much the same kind of creature as Cronos; and as soon as her youngest son, Zeus, was born, she hid him away in a cave on the island of Crete.

'Where is the child?' demanded savage
Cronos, and Rhea gave him a great stone

wrapped in baby-clothes – and he swallowed that, thinking it was Zeus.

But Zeus was safe enough in Crete, guarded by the mountain nymphs, the children of kindly Mother Earth.

When he was fully grown, Zeus sought counsel of the good Titaness Metis, or Thought, who gave him a magic herb which he put into Cronos's wine. It made Cronos very sick, and up came the swallowed children, still very much alive, and all very angry.

The stone came up too, and you may see it to this very day just where it fell, at Delphi. Beside it is another stone which Zeus placed there to mark the centre of the earth: for he let loose two eagles, one from either end of the world, and they met exactly over Delphi.

Then for ten years Zeus, with his brothers and sisters, fought against Cronos and the Titans, and at last beat them, with the aid of the Cyclopes. These were giants with only one eye each, which was in the middle of the forehead. They made thunderbolts which Zeus showered down on his foes; and they made the trident with 11 which Poseidon stirred up the sea to drown his enemies; and they made a helmet of invisibility for Hades, who, when he wore it, could creep up unseen behind the Titans.

When the war was ended, Zeus shut up Cronos and the Titans in a fiery prison under the earth called Tartarus; and in after days the souls of the wicked were sent there to suffer with them.

Zeus and his brothers then cast lots to see which should rule the air, which the sea, and which under the earth: and so Zeus became the King of Heaven, Poseidon ruled the waves, and Hades the realm of the dead.

Then there was peace, and Zeus caused the palaces of the gods to be built: but whether their golden home was on Mount Olympus in the north of Greece, or on some cloud-mountain high up in the heavens, the Greeks were not quite certain.

After this Zeus began to restore the bruised and battered earth, for the Titans had thrown great mountains about, and brought desolation 12 wherever they went.

Not all the Titans had taken part in the war, for the stories say that Helios, who drove the chariot of the Sun, was a Titan, and so was Selene, the Moon, and so too was Ocean, the very sea itself. And there were Metis, or Thought, Themis, or Justice, and Mnemosyne, or Memory, the mother of the Nine Muses, who lived on Mount Helicon. The Muses, of course, attended to the Arts – History, Lyric Poetry, Comedy, Tragedy, Dancing, Love-Poetry, Hymns, Epic, and Astronomy; and they were the special companions of Apollo.

One of the Titans who were imprisoned in Tartarus was Iapetus. He had three sons, two of whom helped Zeus in many ways. The third son, the only one who *looked* like a Titan, was Atlas; who fought against Zeus, and for a punishment was made to stand on top of Mount Atlas in North Africa and hold up the sky on his shoulders.

The two helpful sons of Iapetus were Prometheus and Epimetheus; and the first of these was one of the most important figures in all Greek myth.

Perseus the Gorgon-slayer

PERSEUS was not the Hero for whom Zeus waited, though when he was born Zeus may not have been sure about it: prophecies were uncertain things, or why should he think that the Hero would be an Argive from Argolis? This was the fertile triangle of land through which the river Inachus flows down to the blue bay of Nauplia, and in it the sons of men built three fair cities, Argos, Mycenae, and Tiryns, aided by the Cyclopes, those giant servants of Zeus who had each but one eye, in the centre of the forehead. The huge stones which they raised to form the city walls may be seen, still in place, even to this day.

In Tiryns lived King Acrisius, who had one child only, a lovely girl, called Danae. Being very anxious to have a son to succeed him, Acrisius sent to ask the oracle of Apollo what he had done that this was denied him. His question was not answered; instead the oracle warned him that his daughter would have a son who would kill him.

14

'We'll see about that!' cried Acrisius, and, vowing that Danae should never marry, he shut her up in a tower at Tiryns which was plated all over with brass so that it shone in the sun like gold. The brass plates have gone from it today, but you can still see the brass nails embedded in the stone which once held them in place.

But Zeus visited Danae in a shower of golden rain, and spoke with her out of the shining mist, and they had a son called Perseus who was born there in the prison-tower at Tiryns.

When Acrisius heard that, in spite of all his precautions, he had a grandson, he was filled with anger and fear, and these passions made him cruel. He would not believe that Zeus was the child's father, but said that it was Proteus, his brother, whom he hated, who had stolen the key of the brazen tower and married Danae in secret.

He had a great wooden chest made, and he set Danae in it with the baby in her arms, and pushed it out on to the rippling waters in the Bay of Nauplia.

'It would be a terrible crime to kill my daughter and my grandson,' he said, 'and the Immortals would send a curse upon me. No, I am merely dispatching them across the sea — and if the waves chance to fill the chest and make it sink, I am not to blame!'

Away floated the chest over the blue sea and out of sight of land; and presently the waves began to rise and the wind to blow, and Danae wept with fear and clasped the baby Perseus close in her arms:

'Oh what a fate is yours,' she sobbed, 'and yet you do not cry but sleep as peacefully as ever, feeling no terror of the dreadful place in which we are. You do not fear the heaving sea, nor the salt spray on your hair . . . Oh, perhaps it is because you know that Father Zeus will protect us . . . Then sleep on, sweet babe, for the waves swell only to rock your cradle, and I will pray to Zeus that we may come safely to land.'

All night the chest floated over the sea, and in the morning it was washed up on the shores of the island of Seriphos where Polydectes was king. And there Dictys, the king's brother, who was a fisherman, found Danae and her child, and took them to his home and looked after them.

There Perseus grew up, a strong and noble youth skilled in all manner of things from the craft of the fisherman to the use of the sword. In time King Polydectes heard of them, and fell in love with Danae; but she would not marry him, for he was a cruel and wicked tyrant. At length he decided to take her by force; but this he dared not do because Perseus was always there to guard her.

So he devised a scheme to remove Perseus without incurring any blame for killing him. He held a great feast to which he invited the young men of Seriphos, including Perseus, and they all came bringing rich gifts to the King.

But Perseus had nothing to give, and he alone came empty-handed, so that all the young men mocked him, until his cheeks burnt with shame.

'I'll bring a finer present than any of you!' he cried fiercely.

'That cannot be,' said cunning Polydectes, *'unless you bring me the Gorgon's Head!'*

'That I will!' shouted Perseus. 'I'll bring it, or die in the attempt!'

And with that he rushed out of the palace 17

amid the loud laughter and jeers of Polydectes and his friends, and went down beside the quiet sea to think what he should do.

While he sat there, deep in thought, two Immortals came to him: Athena, tall and stately in her shining helmet, with her polished shield upon her arm; and Hermes with kindly laughter in his eyes, slim and quick of limb, with the winged sandals on his feet.

'Do not grieve, Perseus,' said Hermes, 'for, by the will of Zeus, we are come to help you. See, here I lend you the sharpest weapon in the world, that very sickle of adamant with which Cronos wounded the Sky, and which Zeus used in his battle with Typhon. No lesser blade will smite the head from Medusa the Gorgon.'

'And I,' said Athena in her calm, sweet voice, 'will lend you my shield with which I dazzle the eyes of erring mortals who do battle against my wisdom. Any mortal who looks upon the face of Medusa is turned to stone immediately by the terror of it: but if you look only on her reflection in the shield, all will be well.'

'Rise now,' said Hermes, 'your mother will be

safe until your return, for the good fisherman, Dictys, will protect her – and you have far to travel. First you must visit the Grey Sisters and learn from them how to find the Nymphs who dwell at the back of the North Wind: they will lend you all else that you may need, and will tell you how to find the Gorgons, and how to escape from the two who are immortal, when you have slain Medusa.'

So Perseus hastened away, his heart beating with excitement at the thought of the high adventure which was his, and the great honour which the Immortals had done him.

He came, as Hermes had instructed him, to the lonely cave in the dark north where the three daughters of the Titan Phorcus lived, the Grey Sisters who had been born old women with grey hair, and who had only one eye and one tooth between them.

Perseus stepped quietly up behind them as they sat near the mouth of their cave; and as they passed the single eye from one to another, he took it from an outstretched hand, and then cried aloud:

'Daughters of Phorcus, I have your eye! And I will keep it and leave you for ever in darkness if you do not tell me what I wish to know.'

The Grey Sisters cried aloud in alarm: 'Give us back our eye, and we will swear by Styx to tell you truthfully all you ask. But do not leave us for ever in this terrible darkness!'

So Perseus learnt the way to the magic land at the back of the North Wind and, returning the eye, hastened on his journey.

When he reached the lovely garden of the Northern Nymphs, he was welcomed kindly by them, and he rested for a long time in the paradise where they dwelt for ever young and happy.

But at length he said: 'Fair Nymphs, I must hasten away to kill the Gorgon Medusa and carry her head to wicked King Polydectes. Tell me, I beg of you, where the Gorgons live, and how I may kill Medusa.'

'We will lend you the Shoes of Swiftness,' answered the Nymphs, 'so that you may escape from Medusa's terrible sisters. And we will lend you this magic wallet in which to carry away the head. There is but one thing wanting, and that is the Cap of Hades, the dog-skin cap which makes its wearer invisible.'

Then one of the Nymphs went swiftly down to the Realm of Hades, for she had been Persephone's favourite companion on earth, and could visit the Queen of the Dead whenever she wished, and return at will.

She brought back the Cap of Darkness, so that Perseus now had all things needful, and was ready for his dreadful task.

He bade farewell to the kind Nymphs, and set out on the way which the Grey Sisters had told him, and he came at last to the stony land of the Gorgons. As he drew near to where they lived, he saw all about in the fields and on the roads, the statues of men and beasts which had been living creatures until turned to stone by the deadly glance of the Gorgons.

Then he saw the three terrible sisters lying asleep in the sun with the snakes which grew instead of hair writhing about the head of Medusa, and the dragon-scales which covered her sisters' heads. They had white tusks like pigs and hands of brass; and great golden wings grew from their shoulders.

Wearing the Cap of Darkness, and stepping cautiously, Perseus drew near, looking only at the reflection in Athena's polished shield. Then he trembled indeed as he saw the terrible face of Medusa pictured on the bright surface; but he did not draw back. Still looking only at the reflection, he drew the adamantine sickle and cut off the terrible head at a single blow. Then, quick as could be, he picked it up and dropped it into the wallet which the Nymphs had given him.

But the hissing of the snakes on Medusa's head woke the other two Gorgons, who could not be killed, and they sprang up eager to avenge their sister.

Perseus leapt into the air and sped away on the Shoes of Swiftness as fast as he could go. After him came the Gorgons, screaming with rage, but Perseus fled away and away out over the dark ocean, south, ever south until his terrible pursuers were lost in the distance behind him.

Then Perseus turned east and flew over Africa, across the great empty desert where there was no green thing, and no drop of water. As he went the blood soaked through the magic wallet and dripped behind him, and wherever a drop touched the thirsty sand, it became a green oasis.

Night came, and in the morning as he flew over the sea-shore he beheld what at first he thought was a wonderful statue of a fair girl hewn from the rock just above sea-level.

Swooping down, Perseus found that it was no statue but a living maiden chained naked to the face of the rock, with the little waves creeping up to her feet.

'Chained maiden!' said Perseus gently. 'My heart bleeds for you!'

'Who speaks? Who is it pities poor doomed Andromeda?' she cried wildly.

Perseus had forgotten that he still wore the Cap of Invisibility. Now he removed it swiftly, and hovering above the waves he said:

'Lovely Andromeda, why are you chained here?'

Then, weeping bitterly, she told him how her foolish mother, Cassiopea, had offended the sea-nymphs by her ridiculous boastings, and they 23 had sent a monster to ravage all the sea coast, until King Cepheus, her father, chained her there as a sacrifice, hoping thus to satisfy the creature's fury.

'If I can save you, will you at least remember me?' asked Perseus, who had fallen in love with Andromeda at first sight.

'Do not make me weep, dreaming of deeds that can never be done!' she sobbed.

'Deeds that men deemed impossible have been accomplished, none the less,' he answered. Then he turned quickly away, for he had noticed a ripple in the sea drawing nearer, ever nearer. Perseus, still hovering just above the waves, got ready; and in a few moments the monster raised its head above the water and opened wide its fierce jaws. Then, while Andromeda screamed, and her parents on the cliffs above wept and prayed, Perseus drew the Gorgon's head from his wallet and held it in front of the savage eyes. And the monster sank back still and cold and silent, a long ridge of jagged stone.

Then Perseus returned the head to the magic

wallet, cut Andromeda's chains with the adamantine sickle, and carried her in safety to the cliff top.

There was great rejoicing at the rescue of Andromeda, and King Cepheus readily agreed that Perseus should marry her. So there Perseus stayed for many days, and there was a noble feast at his wedding. But as they sat at the great table, the door was flung suddenly open, and a great man strode in followed by a band of desperadoes all armed with drawn swords:

'Yield up Andromeda to me!' shouted the leader of this band, who was a prince named Phineus. 'She was promised to me, and unless I get her, I'll slaughter every man here, burn the city and carry off the women to be my slaves!'

Then Perseus strode down the hall until he stood in front of Phineus, and taking out the Gorgon's head he turned him and all his followers to stone on the instant.

Not long after this, Perseus and Andromeda set sail for Greece and came at length to the island of Seriphos. Here he found that his mother Danae had been made a slave by 25

Polydectes, while Dictys his kind friend languished in prison.

Leaving Andromeda on the ship, Perseus went alone up to the palace and found Polydectes sitting at meat with the same band of followers who had jeered at him once before.

'Well, if it isn't that landless boaster, Perseus!' cried the king scornfully, while the others laughed and jested at him. 'Have you, by any chance, brought me the present you promised?'

'Yes,' answered Perseus quietly. 'I come, according to my promise, bringing the Gorgon's head.'

'Boaster and liar!' jeered Polydectes. 'Do you think to frighten us with empty words? Show us this wonder – if you can.'

Perseus answered nothing, but pulled the Gorgon's head out of the wallet and held it up for all to see. And afterwards the stone lumps which had once been men were dragged out and dumped on the hillside.

That evening Hermes came to Perseus and received back from him the Sickle and the

Shield and with them the Cap, the Shoes, and

the Wallet. He also took the head of Medusa, which Athena set in the centre of her shield to strike terror into the hearts of the Giants when the long expected invasion should take place.

After this Dictys became King of Seriphos, and married Danae, while Perseus and Andromeda set sail for Argolis. But on the way he stopped at Larissa and took part in the great games which the king of that land was holding.

Perseus distinguished himself greatly in these; but when it came to throwing the round iron disc, he hurled it so hard that it struck an old man who sat watching, and killed him instantly. This, it turned out, was Acrisius, who had left Tiryns in fear that Perseus, on his return, would kill him and so fulfil the oracle.

Sorrowing deeply, Perseus went on his way; and he and Andromeda ruled over Argolis for many years and had numerous children. Among these were Electryon and Alcaeus. The first of these became the father of Alcmena and the second was the father of Amphitryon; and these two cousins married, and went to live in Thebes. And there was a third son called Sthenelus, who late in life had a son called Eurystheus, who ruled over Tiryns and all Argos.

Perseus perished after his battle with Dionysus, and Zeus set him among the stars, with Andromeda beside him: but the son of his granddaughter Alcmena was destined to be the Hero who was to surpass all others in strength and mighty deeds, and who was to help Zeus in his war with the Giants. For this child was Heracles, whom the Romans called Hercules.

The Quest of the Golden Fleece

JASON'S father was the rightful king of Iolcus, but he was deposed by his brother Pelias, the father of Alcestis, who tried to murder the true heir. Jason, however, was smuggled away to the Centaur Chiron who tended him carefully in his mountain cave and trained him in all things suiting a prince.

Pelias, meanwhile, reigned in Iolcus – though not very happily, since an oracle had told him to 'beware of the man with a single sandal', who would cause his death.

When Jason was grown up, he set out for Iolcus to seek his fortune there, and also to find his father and see if he could come to some agreement with his wicked uncle. On the way he came to a ford through the river Anaurus, where the flood-water was running swiftly. An old woman sitting on the bank, cried out when she saw Jason:

'Good sir, will you carry me across; for you are young and strong, with mighty things before you: but I am too old and feeble to battle with the waters of this river.'

'Certainly I will, good mother!' said Jason kindly, and he lifted the old woman on to his shoulders and entered the stream. It was a difficult crossing, and Jason was almost exhausted when he struggled up the further bank, and he had lost one sandal in the mud of the river's bed.

He set down his ancient burden – and then fell on his knees with amazement and awe. For instead of the old woman, the tall and stately form of a shining Immortal stood before him.

'Do not be afraid, Jason,' she said. 'I am Hera, Queen of Heaven, and your friend. Go forward as you are, and speak the words that I shall put into your mouth, and you will become one of the most famous Heroes in all Greece!'

Then she vanished, and Jason went on his way rejoicing, and came to Iolcus in the evening, when Pelias was holding a great feast.

'*The man with one sandal!*' Pelias turned pale and trembled when he saw. And when he learnt that this was his nephew, the rightful heir to the throne, he grew even more afraid. But he hid his fear and his hatred, and welcomed Jason warmly.

'I need just such a man to be my counsellor,' he said heartily. 'And to test your wisdom, let me ask you what, supposing you had the power, you would do if you received an oracle that you were to be deposed by a certain one of your subjects?'

'Do?' exclaimed Jason. 'I would command him to bring home the Golden Fleece from Colchis!'

'Excellent advice!' cried Pelias gleefully. 'You are yourself the man, and you must perform this quest!'

'I will indeed,' said Jason quietly. 'And on my return, I shall fulfil the oracle!'

'I shall yield up the throne to you willingly,' said Pelias, '*when* you return with the Golden Fleece!'

Jason sought the help of Argus, a skilled ship-builder who, with the aid of Athena, made a ship of fifty oars named *Argo* after its maker; and Athena fastened to its prow a magic branch from the oak-tree of Dodona which on occasion could speak, prophesying the future or offering advice.

Next Jason sent heralds throughout Greece calling on the bravest of the young kings and princes to join him on the quest and win immortal fame. From all parts they came trooping to Iolcus – and their names were the names of Heroes still remembered, and their children were the Heroes who fought at Troy.

First came Heracles, with Hylas his esquire; and then Theseus from Athens, and young Castor and Polydeuces from Sparta, with their wild cousins Idas and Lyceus. Telamon came, and Peleus, who had been the companions of Heracles on his expedition against the Amazons; and the wondrous sons of the North Wind, Zetes and Calais, who had wings growing from their shoulders. Admetus came, and Oileus; Laertes the father of Odysseus; Meleager whose strange tale is yet to be told, and Atalanta the Maiden Huntress, the follower of Artemis; Nestor, the only Argonaut to fight at Troy, and many another whose names are recorded in the old books.

There came also the divine singer, Orpheus the son of Apollo. When he played upon his lyre and sang sweetly the wild beasts followed him in friendship, and the very trees and flowers bowed to the power of his music. But his heart was filled with sadness, for his wife Eurydice had been bitten by a snake and died. Orpheus followed her to the Land of the Dead, and at the wonder of his music, Charon ferried him across the Black River Styx and Cerberus let him pass: even Hades was overcome and gave him back his lost Eurydice – but on condition that he did not look behind to see if she was following, until they stood again in the sunlight. But Orpheus, fearing lest Charon had refused to take her across the Styx, looked back once – and Eurydice was lost to him for ever.

When the Heroes were gathered at Iolcus, they hung their shields upon the rails of the *Argo*, and set sail over the dancing waves, while Orpheus played to them, and Tiphys the skilled helmsman guided the ship.

Northwards they sailed, and came to the land of King Cyzicus, who entertained them kindly. 33

When they put to sea again, a great storm took the ship and whirled it around in the darkness till they came to a shore that they did not know, and the inhabitants took them for pirates and attacked them in the night.

Fiercely the battle raged, and the Argonauts (as those who sailed in the *Argo* were called) proved victorious. But what was their grief and horror to find when the day dawned that it was the land of kind King Cyzicus to which they had returned without knowing, and that he and many of his warriors lay dead at their hands.

Sorrowing deeply, they sailed north again, and came to Mysia, not far from Troy, and here Heracles was left behind. For young Hylas went to draw water from a deep pool, and the water-nymphs who dwelt in it fell in love with him and drew him down into the depths to live there with them for ever. Heracles searched for him far and wide, and a great wind rising drove the *Argo* out to sea, so that he was forced to make his way to Colchis over land.

Next the Argonauts visited King Amycus who challenged his guests to a boxing match, and killed each in turn. This time he was met in the ring by Polydeuces, who smote him so hard that he fell to the ground and died.

Sailing onwards they landed in Thrace where the blind King Phineus dwelt, a seer nevertheless, who could look through distance.

'Help us,' they begged, 'and tell us what things to do and what to avoid on our way to Colchis.'

'Help you I will,' said Phineus, 'if you first free me from the Harpies!' Then he set a feast before them: but scarcely had they tasted it when down came the two Harpies – terrible winged women with great claws – who carried off the best of the food, and made the rest uneatable.

Then Zetes and Calais, the winged sons of the North Wind, drew their swords and leapt into the air in pursuit of them, and neither were seen again, though the Harpies never more visited King Phineus.

Now fully instructed as to their way, the Argonauts sailed up the Hellespont and came to the Clashing Rocks which guarded the entrance to the Black Sea. These were great floating masses of blue rock which crashed together and crushed any ship which tried to pass them.

Following King Phineus's advice, Jason let loose a heron, and followed it until they drew near to the Rocks, which were half veiled in mist and spray.

Presently the bird sped between them: the Rocks crashed together, just touching her tail, and then rebounded on either side.

Immediately Tiphys guided the *Argo* through the gap, while every hero strained at his oar. The ship shot between the Rocks, which clashed together only in time to nip the ornament from the end of the stern. From this time on the Clashing Rocks stood still, for it was fated that once a ship had passed them in safety, they could move no more.

The Argonauts sailed on, into the Black Sea, and along its southern coast, until they came to the River Phasis at its eastern end – the river that still runs red down from the Caucasus in memory of the blood which Prometheus shed there for mankind.

36   Up the river they went, and came to the city

of Colchis where Aeetes was king, the fierce son of Helios, whose sister Circe and his daughter Medea were skilled in the black art of witchcraft.

'I will give you the Golden Fleece,' said King Aeetes when Jason told him of their quest, 'if you can yoke my brazenfooted bulls which breathe fire from their nostrils, plough a field with them, and sow it with dragons' teeth!'

That night Jason sat wondering sadly how he was to accomplish this task: for not even Heracles, who had rejoined the Argonauts, could have accomplished it. Then Medea the Witch-Maiden came to him, and said:

'I will tell you how to do this thing, and how to take the Fleece, if you will promise to let me sail back to Greece with you and there become your wife.'

This Jason swore to do, though he had little liking for witches and witchcraft: and Medea instructed him, and gave him a magic ointment which would make him invulnerable and unburnable for a single day.

In the morning, Jason anointed himself with

the ointment and to the amazement of King Aeetes harnessed the bulls without taking any harm. He ploughed the field, and afterwards sowed it with dragons' teeth. But the moment they were sown, the teeth began to grow: and the crop was not corn, but armed men all eager for war and ready to slay Jason.

But Jason remembered what Medea had told him, and flung the helmet which had held the dragons' teeth into the midst of the armed men. At once they began to fight fiercely among themselves, and before long they all lay dead.

'Tomorrow you shall have the Golden Fleece,' promised Aeetes: but before then he plotted to burn the *Argo* and murder the Argonauts.

Medea again came to Jason, and warned him, and in the night she led him and Orpheus to the magic garden where the Golden Fleece hung on the Tree at the World's End, guarded by a dragon – just as the Apples of the Hesperides hung in their garden at the World's opposite end.

It was a dim, mysterious place, high-walled and pillared with the dark boles of mighty trees. Through the dappling moonlight Medea the

Witch-Maiden led the way, until they came to the centre where the Golden Fleece shone in the darkness as it hung from a tree round which coiled a dragon larger and more terrible than any in the world.

'Play and sing!' whispered Medea to Orpheus, and she began to murmur a spell while he touched gently on the strings of his lyre and sang in a sweet low voice his Hymn to Sleep:

'Sleep, king of gods and men,
    Master of all;
Come to mine eyes again,
    Come as I call!
    Sleep, who may loose and bind
    Each as his thrall,
Come to the weary mind,
    Come at my call!
Tamer of toil and woes,
    Healer of all;
Sleep, whence our solace flows,
    Come as I call!
    Brother of all mankind,
    Softly you fall

39

> *Leaving the world behind:*
> *Come at my call!*
> *Sleep, lord of all things made,*
> *Sleep over all*
> *Let your warm wings be laid,*
> *Come as I call!'*

As Orpheus sang it seemed that the very garden slept: the wind grew still; the flowers drooped their heads, and not a leaf stirred. The great gleaming dragon slid slowly from the tree, coil within coil, and, resting its terrible head on a bank of sleeping red poppies, slept for the first and last time in its life.

Only by the charms of Medea did Jason himself remain awake, and when he saw that the dragon slept, he drew near and looked up at the shining Fleece.

Then Medea sprinkled the dragon with her magic brew, and whispered to Jason:

'Climb! Climb swiftly up the coils of its back and take down the Fleece, for my charms will not hold it long!'

So Jason, not without dread, mounted that

terrible ladder into the great ilex-tree and un-hooked the Golden Fleece which had hung there ever since Phrixus stripped it from the magic Ram; and by its light he found his way through the garden.

For Medea, by her charms, called for Hecate, the Immortal Queen of the Witches, and by her help the moon was darkened, and night closed over Colchis like a black cloak.

Going swiftly by secret paths, they came to the river's edge where the *Argo* lay ready, and they stepped on board, Medea taking with her the young Prince Absyrtus, her brother. Then the Argonauts bent to their oars, and rowed so mightily that the stout pine, hewn on Mount Pelion, bent like withies of hazel in their hands as they sped towards the sea.

But suddenly in the darkness behind them the Dragon woke from its charmed sleep, and found that the Golden Fleece had gone. Then it uttered its terrible voice, a hissing and a groaning cry so fearful that all the people of Colchis woke at the sound and the women clutched their children to them and shivered with fear.

King Aeetes, however, guessed what had happened and, dark though it was, launched a swift ship and set off in pursuit of the Argonauts.

'Row! Row!' cried Medea, when she heard the Dragon's cry. 'My father's ships are very swift, and there will be no mercy for any of us if we are taken!'

So they bent to their oars again, and the water was churned into foam as they sped down the Phasis and came with the dawning out into the Black Sea and away to the west.

Before noon they saw the tall ship of King Aeetes drawing up behind them, and in the dim distance others of the Colchian fleet coming in pursuit.

In vain Orpheus played on his lyre to cheer them as they laboured at the oars; and in vain did the winds fill the *Argo's* sail. The great ships of Colchis drew nearer, ever nearer.

Then Medea the Witch did a dreadful thing, while the Argonauts looked on in horror, but dared do nothing because it was she who had saved them, and Jason had sworn to marry her and bring her unhurt to Greece.

She took her brother, the boy prince Absyrtus, and killed him with a sharp sword in plain view of his father, King Aeetes. Then she cut him in pieces and cast the pieces into the sea, for she knew that Aeetes would stop to gather them up so as to give his son due and honourable burial – without which, so they believed, his ghost could find no rest in the Realm of Hades or in the Fields of Elysium.

All happened as she expected. King Aeetes, standing weeping at the prow of his ship, uttered a terrible curse upon Medea and upon all who sailed in the *Argo*; then he halted his fleet to gather up the remains of his son, and the Argonauts sailed on and were lost to view in the wide sea; nor did Aeetes and his fleet find them again.

But Jason bowed his head with shame and misery: for what Medea had done was terrible and not to be forgiven; but now he was bound to her, and had married a Witch who would bring him no good fortune in the end.

The Return of the Argonauts

UNDER the dark shadow of Medea's crime, the Argonauts sailed away into the mysterious distance to the north and west of the Black Sea, and presently a storm overtook the ship, spun it round, and carried it through the darkness, no one knew whither. But, as they were driven between islands and the high cliffs of what might be a great river's mouth, the Magic Branch of Dodona set at the prow spoke to them:

'You who have sinned so deeply cannot escape the wrath of Zeus, nor come to your native land again, until you have visited the Island of Aeaea: for Circe the Enchantress alone can purify you. But the way thither is long and terrible such as no man has sailed before.'

The Argonauts cried out with fear at that eerie voice; then the wind took them again, and darkness closed about them, and they sailed on and on, they knew not where nor whither.

On and ever on they went, sometimes rowing and sometimes blown by the wind; and Orpheus played upon his lyre. Up the river, up and up into the cold north they went; and at length, rowing against the stream until it grew too shallow for them, they landed and carried the *Argo* on their shoulders.

Of that terrible journey little has been told, nor could any of the Argonauts say for certain where they went. But when they were ready to die with weariness, they came to another river flowing north-west and floated down it to a sea where the sun was dimmed by mists, and icicles gathered and hung from the mast and the spars of the *Argo*, and when they landed they saw great white bears.

There were also wild men in those parts; the Laestrygonians, who wore skins and fought with battle-axes, singing wild songs of Odin and the halls of Valhalla, and they foamed at the mouth with berserk rage while they fought.

Shivering with cold, the Argonauts rowed quickly past these frozen coasts where the sun shone at midnight, but did not warm them even at midday. They came then into the Northern Sea and past the land beyond the North Wind, the Ultimate Islands, which in later days were called Britain. Still on they sailed into the Western Ocean where it was said that the Land of Atlantis had sunk beneath the waters not long before; and then south across a stormy bay until at last the sun grew warmer, and one day Heracles cried:

'My friends, we have come back to the known world again! Over yonder stand the two pillars which I set up to mark the entrance to Our Sea, and to the southward Titan Atlas holds up the heavens upon his mountain peak while below is the Garden of the Hesperides!'

He told them of his quest for the Golden Apples, and they marvelled at all he had seen and done. They marvelled still more when he led them to the Garden itself: for there lay the Serpent Ladon, the tip of its tail moving, though it was fifteen years since Heracles had slain it with his poisoned arrow.

The Argonauts rested in that fragrant land until their strength and health came back to them; and they raised altars and sacrificed to the

Immortals in gratitude for bringing them safely through such dangers.

Then they sailed on once more, over the blue Mediterranean Sea, passing between Corsica and Sardinia, and came to Aeaea, the little island where dwelt Medea's aunt, the enchantress Circe.

Now if they had come alone, Circe would have worked some evil enchantment upon the Argonauts, but when she saw Medea she hastened to make them welcome. And when Medea told of her crime and the command of Zeus, spoken by the magic bough, she purified them all of the blood of Absyrtus, and sent them on their way with a load lifted from their hearts.

But their adventures were not yet ended. Near to Aeaea was another island, which is now called Capri, and on it lived the Sirens. These were once maidens who had played with Persephone the Divine Maiden in that fair field of Enna in Sicily from which Hades carried her away to be Queen of the Dead. They had prayed to have wings so as to go through the world in search of her, and Demeter granted their wish. But in 47 some strange way they turned to evil, and so were doomed to live on their beautiful island and lure sailors to their death. They still had wings, but they had the claws and tails of birds also, and they sang so sweetly that no man who heard could resist their singing. For who ever heard that wonderful song forgot all else, plunged into the waves, and swam to shore: and there the Sirens would catch him with their sharp claws, and tear him to pieces. But it was fated that if any one could resist their singing and sail away unhurt, then the Sirens would meet their end.

When the Argonauts drew near and heard the wondrous song of the Sirens, they bent eagerly to their oars, longing only to land on that island and listen to the enchantment of their singing. But Medea knew what fate lay in store for any who set foot on the Isle of the Sirens, and she cried to Orpheus:

'Divine musician, play on your lyre and sing for our lives! Surely you, the son of Apollo, can sing even more sweetly than these creatures of
beauty and evil!'

Orpheus played as never before, and sang such a strain as that which had ravished the ears of Hades and drawn his lost Eurydice from the dead. And the Argonauts listened to his singing, and forgot the Sirens, and were able to turn the ship from that fatal island and sail for the south. All, that is, except Butes, who sprang into the sea and swam towards the Sirens: but Aphrodite took pity on him, and carried him away in time, to become a priest at her shrine in the south of Sicily.

As for the Sirens, as mortal men had withstood their song, Fate came upon them and, like the Sphinx when Oedipus solved her riddle, they flung themselves down from their rock and died. All except two, who had not joined in the song that day, and so lived to sing still, to lure sailors to their doom until Odysseus passed that way on his return from Troy.

On sailed the Argonauts, seeing many other wonders. They passed the cave where lurked Scylla the many-headed monster; though on that day she slept. They passed the whirl-pool of Charybdis in safety, and the Floating Islands which flung out burning rocks, and the Island where Helios, the Sun Titan, kept his milk-white kine with horns of gold, and the happy land of the Phaeacians.

Here they tarried a while, and the wedding of Jason and Medea was celebrated. For while they rested in Phaeacia the ships of King Aeetes arrived, and the Phaeacian King said that while he was ready to give up the daughter of Aeetes, he would defend the wife of Jason! So the Colchians failed of their design, and as Aeetes had sworn to slay them all if they returned without Medea, they settled down and formed a new Kingdom of their own next door to Phaeacia.

The *Argo* sailed again soon after the wedding, and a storm took it as it rounded Cape Malea at the south of Greece, and drove it across the sea to Crete.

Now in the early days the Smith of the Immortals, Hephaestus, had fashioned for the first King Minos a man of brass called Talos, a giant who ran round the island three times in every day and sank any ship which drew near, by 50 hurling great stones on it.

Minos knew how to control this monster, as did all the Kings of Crete until the last Minos had sailed away in pursuit of Daedalus after Theseus killed the Minotaur and escaped from the Labyrinth. But Deucalion, the new King, did not know how to deal with Talos, and he himself had escaped with difficulty from Crete to join the Argonauts and sail with Jason.

The monster Talos was now quite out of control, and Crete was cut off by him from the outer world, for he still ran round the island three times a day, pelting any ship which drew near. At other times he made himself red hot by lying in a bath of fire, and then burned up all that he touched.

Deucalion now begged the other Argonauts to help him to destroy Talos, but not even Heracles could think how to do it.

Then Medea said: 'Only with the help of magic, and by great guile can we overcome Talos. But do just as I say, and all will be well.'

So when she had instructed them, they drew near to the island, and presently Talos appeared, glowing red with heat, a great rock ready in his hands.

Then first of all Orpheus played his sweetest strains, so that Talos paused uncertain, while Medea spoke to him:

'Noble Talos,' said she, 'I am Medea the Witch, and I can make you King of the World, and ruler even over the Immortals, if you will make me your Queen.'

'How can you do that?' rumbled the giant doubtfully.

'Is it not true?' asked Medea, 'that you have but one vein in your body, running from neck to heel, and that instead of blood it contains ichor, the immortal liquid which flows in the veins of the Immortals?'

Talos nodded doubtfully, and Medea went on: 'Although ichor flows in your vein, you are not immortal: but I, by my magic arts, can make you so, if you will let me land safely with one follower.'

Talos agreed to this, and Medea landed, with Poeas who was the smallest man among the Argonauts. If Heracles or Theseus had tried to step ashore, Talos might have suspected some plot, but little Poeas could arouse nobody's suspicion and Talos did not know that he was one of the most skilful archers living – nor that Heracles had lent him his bow and arrows.

Once on the shore, Poeas wandered away and settled himself quietly out of sight among the rocks. But Medea took a sickle with a blade of brass and began to gather herbs with which to make a magic brew. She mixed them in a cauldron, squeezing the milk-white juices from them, and singing an incantation. Next she stripped off her clothes, bound up her jet-black hair with wreaths of ivy, and bent over the cauldron, chopping the herbs and roots and singing wildly.

Talos was fascinated by the lovely Witch-wife and her magic brew; he drew nearer and nearer, but still mistrustfully. For in his heel was set a brass nail, like a stopper, which prevented the ichor from escaping, and he feared greatly lest any one should touch it.

Medea had soon brewed her magic draught, and now she held it out to Talos in a cup: 'Drink!' she said. 'It is the wine of Immortality!'

And Talos was so bewitched that he took the

cup and drained it. But it brought to him only a great drowsiness so that presently he was reeling about as if drunken, but still determined not to fall asleep lest any one should draw out the nail.

Then Poeas rose, fitted an arrow to the bow, and shot with such skill that the arrow struck the nail in Talos's heel and loosened it so that it fell to the ground and the ichor gushed out.

At this Talos cried aloud and groped for the nail: but the magic brew was too strong for him, and he could not find it, and presently he lay cold and still – an image of brass, nothing more.

After this the Argonauts landed in Crete and were entertained lavishly by Deucalion before setting sail for Iolcus which they reached without further adventures.

There they parted, though very soon a number of them met again for the adventure of the Calydonian Boar which, at his homecoming, Meleager found was ravaging his land.

Jason did not live to enjoy the old age of honour which was his due. He died childless and 54 alone, with the curse of Aeetes upon him, for there was no purification which could free him wholly from the guilt of Absyrtus's murder.

When he returned to Iolcus he found his old father was dead, and Pelias still ruling there. Jason was content to let him remain as king for the rest of his life, but Medea the Witch wished to be queen. So while Jason was away at Calydon she said to the daughters of Pelias: 'You know my magic powers: would you like to learn from me how to make your father young again?'

At first they mistrusted her. So Medea mixed a magic brew in a great cauldron; and she took an old ram, so old it could hardly walk. She killed it, cut it into small pieces, and threw them into the cauldron. And at once there leapt out of it, a young lamb, strong and bold and frisky.

Then the daughters of Pelias doubted her no longer. They took their old father, killed him and cut him up. But when they placed the pieces in the cauldron, Pelias remained as dead as ever — for Medea had not taught them her evil spell.

But when the people of Iolcus discovered what Medea had done, they banished her and Jason, who wandered away to Corinth. There

Jason had a chance of a new kingdom: for the king had only one child, the maiden Glauce.

'You shall marry her and rule this land,' said the king, 'if you will send away that evil Witch, Medea.'

Jason, who had never loved Medea, and by now hated her for her cruelty and wickedness, consented to this, and Medea appeared to agree, but she gave Glauce a magic wedding dress which burned her to death the moment she put it on, and burned her father also who tried to save her.

Then Medea killed her own and Jason's two sons, and fled away in a chariot drawn by flying dragons.

But Jason became an outcast, and in his wanderings he returned to where the old ship *Argo* was drawn up on the beach.

'You are my only friend,' he said sadly as he sat down to rest in the shade of the ship. There he fell asleep, and while he slept the front of the ship, grown rotten with age, fell suddenly on his head and killed him.

PENGUIN CHILDREN'S 60s